*This book
is dedicated to:*

_____

© 2002 Havoc Publishing
San Diego, California
U.S.A.

Text by F. E. Skarka

ISBN 0-7416-1239-9

www.havocpub.com

Made in China

*In dreams
you can be everything
you ever want to be.*

Dreams begin
with a simple thought
and in time they grow.

*It requires
a lot of courage
and a lot of
patience as well,*

to start
with a wish
and let it remain
in your heart.

A wish
is an opportunity
to change tomorrow.

The dreams
you wish today

will come true

tomorrow.

*Your wishes will
take you places
you thought you
would never go.*

One wish will
help you through
the most difficult
of days.

*Your dreams
can last forever,
as long as you
have hope.*

You are never poor
as long as
you have your dreams.

*Never regret
a dream.*

Remember,
wishes need love
and a little care.

You can dream
of going to places
you have seen in books,
or you can dream
of staying in the comfort
of your own home.

No matter
how great or small
your dreams,
they always bring
happiness.

You can
share your wishes
with everyone

*but no one
can take
them away.*

The only things
you need to wish for

are a loving heart
and an open mind.

The sad times
are not so lonely
when shared with
a wish.

Hope is brighter
than any star
when the night is dark.

If you want
to change the world,
begin with
a dream.

*Believe
in the power
of your dreams,*

*even if it is
the only thing
you do.*

Dreams are many,
and they stretch
across the sky.

*Dreams throw light
from the heavens
onto the earth below.*

A dream
can go anywhere,
but it must
come from the heart.

A dream
holds more beauty
than a flower garden
in spring.

Nothing in life
is more important

*than the hope
of your dreams.*

Every great
achievement
began with an
impossible dream.

When you feel
hope is gone,
remember dreams
do come true.

Hold on to your hope
because it is
the future.

*Dare
to dream;*

*it is the
first step
to success.*

Your dreams
are a lot like keys
that open
many doors.

All you need
to do is believe
that your dreams
can take you anywhere.

Every wish
is a beginning,
a chance
to start anew.

*Today began
with a wish
that tomorrow
will come true.*

*If you want
to touch the stars,*

*you must first
dream of flying.*

Life is full
of dreams
that keep you
going strong.

Sometimes
your dreams are right
when all else
is wrong.

Dreams are
like roads that
lead you to places;

some that
you know very well
and some
you have never
been before.

*Take a dream
with you
wherever you go*

and you will always
travel first class.

Like the sun
that rises at dawn,
my dreams
bring me hope.

Few things
are more tragic
than living
without dreams.

Nothing
is more important
than believing
in your dreams.

Dreams pass through
your thoughts

like sailboats

upon a sea,

A dream
will last forever,
through all
of eternity.

Dreams go
on and on
for as long
as you believe.

Follow your dreams
over the
highest hills

and through
the lowest valleys
on the road
toward happiness.

The dreams
of today

make tomorrow
so much better.

When you need a friend,
a wish will extend
a hand.
When you are sad,
a wish will help
you smile.

When you are wandering,
a wish will lead
you home.

The future
belongs to those
who believe in the
beauty of their dreams.

-Eleanor Roosevelt

If you have
never smiled,
then you have
never hoped.

Dreams go on
like a heart,

beating with
hope and love.

If you are
brave enough
to dream,

anything
is possible.

The future
beams bright
on the horizon
with your dreams
for tomorrow.

Your dreams
will never
slip away

*if you hold on
to them tightly.*

Like flowers
in a garden,
hope grows
in a heart.

A wish
is a promise
that tomorrow
will be better
than today.

*You need
nothing more in life
than the ability
to hope.*